Robin Grant

SINGING 'N' SWINGING

A jazz suite for B flat clarinet and piano

The Associated Board of the Royal Schools of Music

Dedicated to the memory of Angora

1
Two Seater

CLARINET IN B♭

ROBIN GRANT

Moderato, with swing ♩.=116

AB 2230

2
Remember December

3
Dancing in the Moonlight

4
When the last petal falls

5
San Remo's

6
Goodbye Valentine Valley

Robin Grant

SINGING 'N' SWINGING

A jazz suite for B flat clarinet and piano

The Associated Board of the Royal Schools of Music

CONTENTS

Dedicated to the memory of Angora

1
Two Seater

ROBIN GRANT

2nd time to ⊕

2
Remember December

3
Dancing in the Moonlight

4
When the last petal falls

5
San Remo's

2nd time to ⊕

6
Goodbye Valentine Valley